World Book

Prairie College School

Learn about

SIZE

"Poldy" is a trademark
of World Book, Inc.

World Book, Inc.
525 W. Monroe
Chicago, IL 60661

For information on other
World Book products,
call 1-800-255-1750.

ISBN: 0-7166-6101-2
LC: 95-61312

Printed in Mexico

1 2 3 4 5 6 7 8 9 10 99 98 97 96 95

Learn about
SIZE

World Book, Inc.

a Scott Fetzer company

Chicago   London   Sydney   Toronto

Meet Poldy
and his friends

Poldy the scarecrow was made to scare birds away from a farmer's field. But the birds were not frightened by Poldy. In fact, three birds named Wagtail, Crow, and Seagull became his friends.

When the weather grew cold, Poldy's friends prepared to fly away to wonderful, warm places all over the world. The three birds wanted Poldy to go with them, so they worked together to teach him how to fly. Then Poldy and his friends flew away to see and learn about the world.

In **Learn about Size**, Poldy and his friends travel to Africa.

Poldy took a ride in a balloon. He had never seen a balloon before. It was big and round and brightly colored. It floated high in the sky, far above the ground.

Poldy had a wonderful
view. He could see all kinds
of animals on the ground
below. They looked very little
from so high up.
Then the balloon floated
down and down toward the
grassy plain.

A big elephant reached
up with his long trunk. He
tried to catch the ropes on
the basket.

"You're very big and fat, just like me," he said to the balloon. "Will you stay and talk?"

But the balloon floated
on. It passed a tall giraffe
who was chewing leaves
from the top of a tree. The
giraffe reached up with
her long neck.

"You're very tall, just like me," she said to the balloon. "Will you stay and talk?"

But the balloon floated on.
"Hold on!" called Poldy to
his friends, the birds.
The balloon landed with
a great bump on the grass,
scattering many animals. It
flapped as the wind tugged
and pulled, and the hot air
escaped. The balloon blew
this way and that, and then
it was still.

It was quite still, except for the basket. Something was moving inside the basket, which had landed upside down.

"There's something underneath," said Wagtail. "It must be Poldy."

"Oh, dear," said Crow. "We can't leave him there. We'll have to lift the basket and help him out."

The animals gathered
around. Everyone wanted
to help.

"We have long legs," said the ostrich and the flamingo. "We could kick the basket over."

"We have big teeth," said
the lion and the crocodile.
"We could bite a hole in it."

"We have large horns," said the buffalo and the rhinoceros. "We could rip the basket to pieces!"

"We have fat bodies," said the hippopotamus and the elephant. "We could push it over!"

"Now, just a minute!" said
Crow firmly. "This all sounds
very dangerous. I'm sure there's
an easier way!"

Wagtail was watching the basket. "I think we should hurry," he said. "I don't think Poldy likes being under there!"

"We have short legs,"
said the porcupine and the
pangolin. "We could dig a
tunnel under the basket."

"We have little teeth,"
said the dormouse and the
shrew. "We could nibble a
hole in it."

"We have small beaks," said the gray parrot and the honeyguide. "We could peck our way into the basket."

"We have thin bodies," said the snake and the lizard. "We could wriggle underneath."

"And what good will it do," snapped Seagull, "if you all end up under the basket, too?"

"Well," said all the animals,
"since you don't need our help,
we'll be on our way. Good luck!"

"Oh, dear," said a worried Wagtail. "Who's going to help us now? I do hope Poldy's all right!"

"Of course I'm all right," said Poldy, peeking out from under the basket. "I was just hiding until all those animals went away and it was safe to come out!"

Big and little

Say the names of these big animals.

elephant

ostrich

buffalo

rhinoceros

Say the names of these little animals.

shrew

gray parrot

snake

dormouse

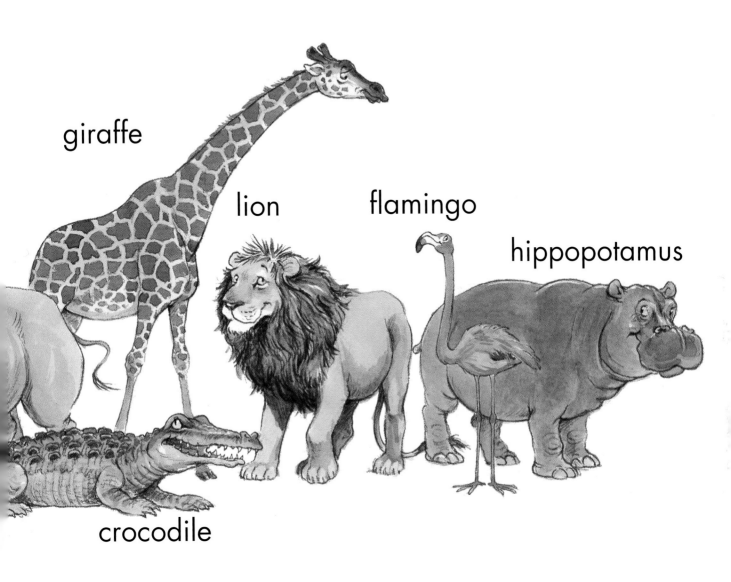

giraffe

lion

flamingo

hippopotamus

crocodile

porcupine

pangolin

honeyguide

lizard

Can you find the big animals?
Can you find the little animals?

Parent notes

At a very early age, children begin to learn about size. Your child may already know some words to describe simple ideas of size, such as *big, small, fat,* and *thin.* These ideas form an important part of children's understanding of the world around them.

In **Learn about Size,** Poldy flies away in a hot-air balloon. When the balloon lands on the grassy plains of Africa, Poldy and his friends find many animals of different sizes. Poldy's adventure provides many opportunities to explore the ideas of size. Your child's vocabulary and understanding of size will be extended by comparing and contrasting the animals Poldy and his friends encounter. As you read the story, use the pictures in the book as starting points for discussions with your child:

All about size

Can you find a big animal?
Can you find a small animal?
Which animals have long legs?
Which animals have long necks?
Why can the giraffe eat leaves from the treetops?
Can you see an animal with big teeth?
Can you see an animal with little teeth?

All about comparing sizes

Is the hippopotamus as big as the elephant?
Which is the tallest animal?
Which is the smallest animal?
Which is the fattest animal?
Which is the thinnest animal?
Can you find an animal that could fit into the balloon basket?
Can you find an animal that could not fit into the balloon basket?

Learning together

Sizes can be described in many ways. Encourage your child to use a variety of words to describe sizes. For example, *big* can also be *large, huge, enormous,* or *gigantic.* Finding synonyms in this way will enrich your child's vocabulary and understanding. Give your child opportunities to understand and experience other concepts of size, such as *wide* and *narrow, thick* and *thin, long* and *short, shallow* and *deep.* Here are some activities that will help you to explore these ideas with your child:

Compare sizes within your family. Who is the tallest? Who has the smallest feet? Who has the longest hair?

Find opportunities during the day for your child to sort and match objects of different sizes. For example, put all the small spoons together, or put all the big plates together.

Make a size scrapbook using pictures cut from old magazines, cards, and catalogs. You could have a page of long things and a page of short things, a page of big things and a page of little things.

When you are out walking, ask your child to describe the journey using size words. For example, you may walk down a *short* path past a *tall* tree and turn onto a *wide* street.

Use clay and toothpicks to reinforce ideas of size. Ask your child to make a *long* snake, a *fat* elephant, and a *small* porcupine.